LATIN'S NOT SO TOUGH!

LEVEL TWO

A Classical Latin Worktext
by
Karen Mohs

Dear Parent/Teacher:

Welcome to the Latin Workbook Level Two!

This workbook concentrates on words. A fifty word vocabulary is introduced and thoroughly reviewed. These words will form the building blocks for the concepts to be learned in Level Three.

Remove the flashcard pages at the end of the workbook, cut out the letters/words, and copy, paste, or tape them onto 3 by 5 inch cards.

Begin use of flashcards after the first workbook page. As the child learns each new letter, diphthong, special consonant, or word, add it to the flashcard stack. To record and encourage consistency, your student should put a check mark in the box at the bottom of each page when daily flashcard work is completed. Please refer to "Flashcard Tips" in the appendix.

An answer key is available, as well as quizzes/exams, flashcards on a ring, and an audio pronunciation CD or cassette tape.

References for this series include *First Year Latin* by Charles Jenney, Jr., *Second Year Latin* by Charles Jenney, Jr., and *The New College Latin & English Dictionary* by John C. Traupman, Ph.D.

Keep having fun!

ISBN 1-931842-55-8

Greek 'n' Stuff
P.O. Box 882
Moline, IL 61266-0882
www.greeknstuff.com

Revised 9/04

This workbook
belongs to me:

_____

(student's name)

because
I'M LEARNING LATIN
Level Two!

TABLE OF CONTENTS

Appendix

LET'S REVIEW THE LATIN ALPHABET

Ā ā

As you write the letters across each line, say the sound of "**a**" in *father*.

Ā

ā

A a

As you write the letters across each line, say the sound of "**a**" in *idea*.

A

a

B b

As you write the letters across each line, say the sound of "**b**" in *boy*.

B

b

Start your flashcard deck with these cards. Review them every day.
(See back of workbook.)
☐ I practiced my flashcards today.

MORE ALPHABET REVIEW

As you write the letters across each line, say the sound of **"c"** in *cat*.

C

c

As you write the letters across each line, say the sound of **"d"** in *dog*.

D

d

As you write the letters across each line, say the sound of **"ey"** in *obey*.

Ē

ē

☐ I practiced my flashcards today. (Add the new cards.)

Latin Workbook - Level 2
Copyright © 1997 by Karen Mohs

MORE ALPHABET REVIEW

As you write the letters across each line, say the sound of "**e**" in *bet*.

E

e

As you write the letters across each line, say the sound of "**f**" in *fan*.

F

f

As you write the letters across each line, say the sound of "**g**" in *go*.

G

g

☐ I practiced my flashcards today. (Add the new cards.)

MORE ALPHABET REVIEW

As you write the letters across each line, say the sound of "**h**" in *hat*.

H

h

As you write the letters across each line, say the sound of "**i**" in *machine*.

Ī

ī

As you write the letters across each line, say the sound of "**i**" in *sit*.

I

i

☐ I practiced my flashcards today. (Add the new cards.)

4

MORE ALPHABET REVIEW

As you write the letters across each line, say the sound of "**k**" in *king*.

K

k

As you write the letters across each line, say the sound of "**l**" in *land*.

L

l

As you write the letters across each line, say the sound of "**m**" in *man*.

M

m

☐ I practiced my flashcards today. (Add the new cards.)

MORE ALPHABET REVIEW

As you write the letters across each line, say the sound of "**n**" in *nut*.

N

n

As you write the letters across each line, say the sound of "**o**" in *note*.*

ō

ō

As you write the letters across each line, say the sound of "**o**" in *omit*.*

O

o

*Although both Latin "o" sounds are "long," the ō as in *note* is held longer than the o as in *omit*.

☐ I practiced my flashcards today. (Add the new cards.)

6

MORE ALPHABET REVIEW

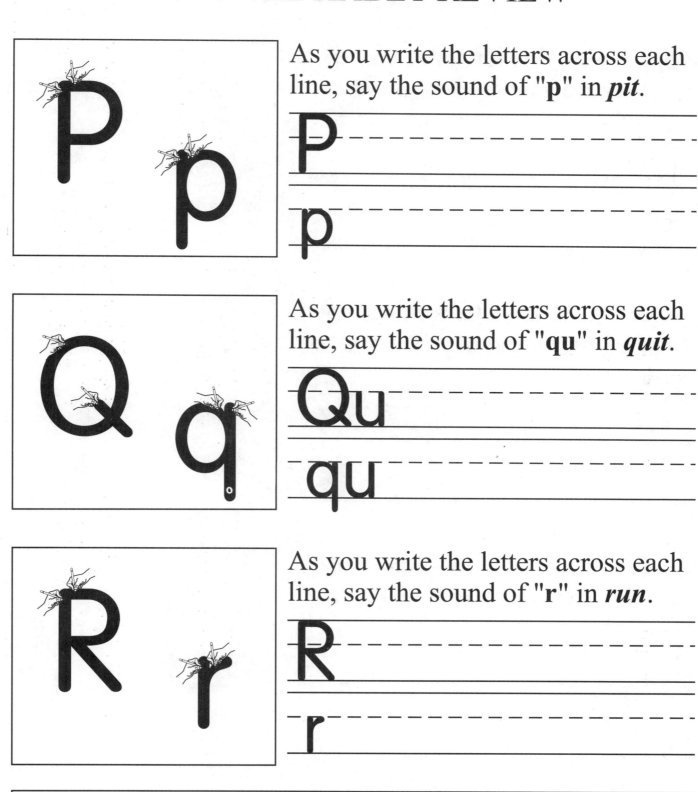

As you write the letters across each line, say the sound of "**p**" in *pit*.

P

p

As you write the letters across each line, say the sound of "**qu**" in *quit*.

Qu

qu

As you write the letters across each line, say the sound of "**r**" in *run*.

R

r

☐ I practiced my flashcards today. (Add the new cards.)

MORE ALPHABET REVIEW

As you write the letters across each line, say the sound of "**s**" in *sit*.

S

s

As you write the letters across each line, say the sound of "**t**" in *tag*.

T

t

As you write the letters across each line, say the sound of "**u**" in *rule*.

Ū

ū

☐ I practiced my flashcards today. (Add the new cards.)

8

MORE ALPHABET REVIEW

As you write the letters across each line, say the sound of "**u**" in *put*.

As you write the letters across each line, say the sound of "**w**" in *way*.

As you write the letters across each line, say the sound of "**ks**" in *socks*.

☐ I practiced my flashcards today. (Add the new cards.)

MORE ALPHABET REVIEW

As you write the letters across each line, form your lips to say **"oo"** but say **"ee"** instead. (Hold the sound longer than Latin y.)

Ȳ

ȳ

As you write the letters across each line, form your lips to say **"oo"** but say **"ee"** instead. (Hold the sound shorter than Latin ȳ.)

Y

y

As you write the letters across each line, say the sound of **"dz"** in *adze*.

Z

z

☐ I practiced my flashcards today. (Add the new cards.)

LET'S PRACTICE

Match the letters with their sounds.

Uu	**d** in *dog*	Bb	**g** in *go*
Oo	**u** in *rule*	Gg	**p** in *pit*
Ūū	**u** in *put*	Kk	**b** in *boy*
Dd	**o** in *omit*	Tt	**k** in *king*
Ōō	**h** in *hat*	Pp	**w** in *way*
Xx	**ks** in *socks*	Vv	**c** in *cat*
Ff	**o** in *note*	Cc	**m** in *man*
Hh	**n** in *nut*	Aa	**t** in *tag*
Ī ī	**s** in *sit*	Mm	**a** in *idea*
Nn	**f** in *fan*	Ll	**e** in *bet*
Ss	**i** in *machine*	Ee	**ey** in *obey*
Ȳ ȳ	**r** in *run*	Yy	**qu** in *quit*
Rr	**i** in *sit*	Āā	**a** in *father*
I i	**dz** in *adze* form lips to say "oo," say "ee" instead (held longer)	Ēē	**l** in *land* form lips to say "oo," say "ee" instead (held shorter)
Zz		Qq	

☐ I practiced my flashcards today.

Latin Workbook - Level 2
Copyright © 1997 by Karen Mohs

11

LET'S REVIEW LATIN DIPHTHONGS

ae

As you write the diphthong ae, say the "*aye*" sound.

ae

ae

As you write the diphthong au, say the "**ow**" sound in *now*.

au

au

au

ei

As you write the diphthong ei, say the "**ei**" sound in *neighbor*.

ei

ei

☐ I practiced my flashcards today. (Add the new cards.)

12

MORE LATIN DIPHTHONGS

As you write the diphthong eu, say "*ay-oo*" as one syllable.

eu

eu

| eu |

As you write the diphthong oe, say the "**oy**" sound in *joy*.

| oe |

oe

oe

As you write the diphthong ui, say the "**uee**" sound in *queen*.

ui

ui

| ui |

☐ I practiced my flashcards today. (Add the new cards.)

LET'S PRACTICE

Write the Latin letters for the sounds.

1. Latin _____ sounds like **uee** in *queen*.

2. Latin _____ sounds like **ei** in *neighbor*.

3. Latin _____ sounds like *aye*.

4. Latin _____ sounds like *ay-oo* (in one syllable).

5. Latin _____ sounds like **ow** in *now*.

6. Latin _____ sounds like **oy** in *joy*.

☐ I practiced my flashcards today.

Latin Workbook - Level 2
Copyright © 1997 by Karen Mohs

LET'S REVIEW SPECIAL CONSONANTS

As you write the consonants bs, say the "*ps*" sound.

bs

bs

bt

As you write the consonants bt, say the "*pt*" sound.

bt

bt

As you write the consonants ch, say the "**ch**" sound in *character*.

ch

ch

ch

☐ I practiced my flashcards today. (Add the new cards.)

MORE SPECIAL CONSONANTS

gu

As you write the consonants gu, say the "**gu**" sound in *anguish*.

gu

gu

i

As you write the consonant i, say the "**y**" sound in *youth*.

i

i

ph

As you write the consonants ph, say the "**ph**" sound in *phone*.

ph

ph

☐ I practiced my flashcards today. (Add the new cards.)

16

MORE SPECIAL CONSONANTS

As you write the consonants su, say the "**su**" sound in *suave*.

su

su

su

As you write the consonants th, say the "**th**" sound in *thick*.

th

th

th

Write six Latin diphthongs.

_____ _____ _____ _____ _____

_____ _____ _____ _____ _____

_____ _____ _____ _____ _____

Write eight Latin special consonants.

_____ _____ _____ _____ _____

_____ _____ _____ _____ _____

_____ _____ _____ _____ _____

☐ I practiced my flashcards today. (Add the new cards.)

LET'S PRACTICE

Match the letters with their sounds.

Qq	**su** in *suave*	eu	**ks** in *socks*
su	**g** in *go*	Pp	*ay-oo* (in one syllable)
ui	**qu** in *quit*	I i	**gu** in *anguish*
Ū ū	**uee** in *queen*	Xx	**ch** in *character*
Gg	**u** in *put*	gu	**p** in *pit*
bt	**u** in *rule*	ch	**i** in *machine*
Uu	*pt*	Ī ī	**i** in *sit*
i	**ey** in *obey*	ei	**ei** in *neighbor*
bs	**e** in *bet*	oe	**o** in *omit*
E e	**y** in *youth*	Oo	**dz** in *adze*
au	*ps*	Ō ō	**oy** in *joy*
Ē ē	**ph** in *phone*	Zz	**o** in *note*
ph	**ow** in *now*	Aa	**th** in *thick*
V v	*aye*	th	**a** in *father*
ae	**w** in *way*	Ā ā	**a** in *idea*

☐ I practiced my flashcards today.

LET'S PRACTICE

Circle the words with the Latin sounds.

ch	arch car child	bt	able slept debt	th	the this throng
g	gem age good	ei	diet reign seige	v	wish never vast
oe	foil poet toe	au	slow taught cow	ō	knob vote often
c	mice can race	bs	hips tabs ribs	ī	right hit clean
ui	tweet built suit	su	suit sun swim	ē	get say feet

☐ I practiced my flashcards today.

LET'S PRACTICE

Circle the correct Latin letters below the sounds.

u in *put*		th in *thick*		ey in *obey*	
Ūū	Uu	th	t	Ēē	Ee
a in *idea*		**ow in *now***		**i in *machine***	
Aa	Āā	au	ae	I i	Ī ī
uee in *queen*		**i in *sit***		**o in *note***	
ue	ui	Ī ī	I i	Ōō	Oo
u in *rule*		**a in *father***		**su in *suave***	
Ūū	Uu	Āā	Aa	gu	su
o in *omit*		**e in *bet***		**oy in *joy***	
Oo	Ōō	Ēē	Ee	oe	eu

□ I practiced my flashcards today.

Latin Workbook - Level 2
Copyright © 1997 by Karen Mohs

puella

means

girl

Write the Latin word that means **girl**.

_____

- -

_____

Circle the Latin words that mean **girl**.

puela	peula	peula
puella	pulla	pulla
peula	puella	peulla
peulla	pluea	puella

☐ I practiced my flashcards today. (Add the new card.)

LET'S PRACTICE

Fill in the missing letters on the Latin word that means **girl**.

_u_l_a

Draw a line from the Latin word to its meaning.

puella

man
child
girl

Draw a picture of a **puella**.

☐ I practiced my flashcards today.

vocō

means

I call

Write the Latin word that means **I call**.

_____

– –

_____

Check the blank if the sentence is true.

_____ 1. vocō means **I want**.
_____ 2. puella means **child**.
_____ 3. vocō means **I call**.
_____ 4. puella means **girl**.

☐ I practiced my flashcards today. (Add the new card.)

LET'S PRACTICE

Circle the Latin words to match the meanings.

I call	girl
vacō	pellua
vocō	peulla
vocā	puella

Unscramble the words and write them beside their meanings.

1. elpaul

2. coōv

I call _____

girl _____

Write the meanings of the Latin words.

1. puella _____

2. vocō _____

☐ I practiced my flashcards today.

puer

means

boy

Write the Latin word that means **boy**.

_____

- -

_____

Connect the words to the meanings in the ovals.

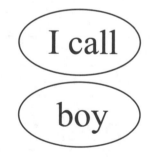

puer
puella
dō
vocō

(I call)

(boy)

puella
vocō
puer
dō

☐ I practiced my flashcards today. (Add the new card.)

LET'S PRACTICE

Fill in the missing letters. Then write what the words mean.

_ue_

It means _____

p__ll_

It means _____

_o_ō

It means _____

———————◆◆◆———————

Circle the Latin words to match the meanings.

I call	vocō	vacō
	voccō	voco

boy	pēur	peur
	pour	puer

girl	pullea	puela
	puella	pella

☐ I practiced my flashcards today.

26

dō

means

I give

Write the Latin word that means **I give**.

_____

- -

_____

Circle **yes** or **no**.

yes no   1. **puer** means **boy**.

yes no   2. **dō** means **I do**.

yes no   3. **puella** means **dress**.

yes no   4. **vocō** means **I call**.

☐ I practiced my flashcards today. (Add the new card.)

LET'S PRACTICE

Match the Latin words to their meanings.

___ 1. puer   a. girl

___ 2. vocō   b. I give

___ 3. dō   c. I call

___ 4. puella   d. boy

Write the meanings of the Latin words.

1. dō   _____

2. puer   _____

3. vocō   _____

4. puella   _____

☐ I practiced my flashcards today.

agricola

means

farmer

Write the Latin word that means **farmer**.

_____

– –

_____

Draw lines from the words to their meanings.

vocō	farmer
agricola	boy
puer	I call
dō	I give

☐ I practiced my flashcards today. (Add the new card.)

LET'S PRACTICE

Unscramble the words and write them beside their meanings.

1. eurp   I call _____

2. lalupe   I give _____

3. covō   boy _____

4. ōd   girl _____

Circle the Latin words to match the meanings.

farmer
vocō
puer
agricola

girl
puella
puer
agricola

I call
agricola
vocō
puer

I give
dō
puella
vocō

boy
puella
vocō
puer

☐ I practiced my flashcards today.

30

aqua

means

water

Write the Latin word that means **water**.

_____

- -

_____

Write the Latin words.

farmer _____   I give _____

water _____   boy _____

☐ I practiced my flashcards today. (Add the new card.)

LET'S PRACTICE

Fill in the blanks with the Latin words from the box.

aqua	agricola	dō

1. _____ means **I give**.

2. _____ means **farmer**.

3. _____ means **water**.

Circle the meanings of the Latin words.

aqua	
color	water

puella	
girl	boy

puer	
girl	boy

vocō	
I call	I do

dō	
I call	I give

agricola	
farmer	farm

☐ I practiced my flashcards today.

32

est

means

he is, she is, it is, there is

Write the Latin word that means **he is**.

_____

– – – – – – – – – – – – – – – – – – – –

_____

Circle **yes** or **no**.

yes   no   1. aqua means **blue**.

yes   no   2. est means **she is**.

yes   no   3. dō means **I make**.

yes   no   4. agricola means **farmer**.

☐   I practiced my flashcards today. (Add the new card.)

LET'S PRACTICE

Write the meanings of the Latin words.

1. vocō   _____
2. puella   _____
3. dō   _____
4. aqua   _____
5. puer   _____
6. est   _____
7. agricola _____

———————•◆•———————

Unscramble the words and write them beside their meanings.

1. aaqu   boy   _____

2. coōv   water _____

3. rupe   he is _____

4. tes   I call _____

☐ I practiced my flashcards today.

fēmina

means

woman

Write the Latin word that means **woman**.

_____

- -

_____

Circle the Latin words that mean **woman**.

fēmina	fīmena	fēnema
fēnima	feminā	femīna
femina	fēmana	fēmina
fāmina	fēmina	fēmena

☐ I practiced my flashcards today. (Add the new card.)

LET'S PRACTICE

Fill in the blanks with the Latin words from the box.

puer	fēmina	est

1. _____ means **there is**.

2. _____ means **boy**.

3. _____ means **woman**.

Circle **yes** or **no**.

yes no   1. puella means **girl**.
yes no   2. agricola means **gold**.
yes no   3. fēmina means **woman**.
yes no   4. puer means **little**.
yes no   5. vocō means **win**.
yes no   6. est means **there is**.
yes no   7. aqua means **water**.
yes no   8. dō means **I give**.

☐ I practiced my flashcards today.

36

et

means

and

Write the Latin word that means **and**.

— —

Circle the Latin words to match the meanings.

woman	and	it is
fēmina	aqua	et
fortūna	et	est
fīlius	ad	sed

☐ I practiced my flashcards today. (Add the new card.)

LET'S PRACTICE

Circle the Latin words to match the meanings.

and	ete	et
	est	ēt

he is, she is, it is, there is	est	ēst
	ete	et

boy	puerre	peur
	puer	peurre

Write the Latin words.

woman _____

I call _____

she is _____

water _____

I give _____

girl _____

farmer _____

and _____

☐ I practiced my flashcards today.

silva

means

forest

Write the Latin word that means **forest**.

_____

- -

_____

Fill in the missing letters. Then write what the words mean.

fē__i__a

It means _____

s_lv_

It means _____

☐ I practiced my flashcards today. (Add the new card.)

LET'S PRACTICE

Match the Latin words to their meanings.

___	1. est	a.	woman
___	2. agricola	b.	water
___	3. puer	c.	forest
___	4. dō	d.	girl
___	5. silva	e.	I give
___	6. vocō	f.	I call
___	7. puella	g.	boy
___	8. fēmina	h.	farmer
___	9. aqua	i.	there is

Connect the words to the meanings in the ovals.

est
equus
et
sunt
fortūna
silva
fēmina
sed

(and)
(she is)
(forest)
(woman)

fortūna
et
sed
est
silva
equus
sunt
fēmina

☐ I practiced my flashcards today.

LET'S REVIEW

Write the Latin letters for the sounds.

o in *note* _____

u in *rule* _____

y in *youth* _____

ks in *socks* _____

pt _____

n in *nut* _____

e in *bet* _____

c in *cat* _____

o in *omit* _____

ow in *now* _____

i in *sit* _____

w in *way* _____

oy in *joy* _____

ey in *obey* _____

u in *put* _____

a in *idea* _____

aye _____

a in *father* _____

t in *tag* _____

ps _____

☐ I practiced my flashcards today.

LET'S PRACTICE

Draw a picture of a **fēmina** standing in a **silva** with a **puer** and a **puella**.

☐ I practiced my flashcards today.

īnsula

means

island

Write the Latin word that means **island**.

_____

- -

_____

Draw lines from the words to their meanings.

silva	and
īnsula	forest
fēmina	island
et	woman

☐ I practiced my flashcards today. (Add the new card.)

LET'S PRACTICE

Check the blank if the sentence is true.

_____ 1. est means **it is**.
_____ 2. puer means **fear**.
_____ 3. agricola means **farmer**.
_____ 4. īnsula means **island**.
_____ 5. et means **I ate**.
_____ 6. fēmina means **woman**.
_____ 7. silva means **forest**.
_____ 8. dō means **I do**.

Write the Latin words.

he is _____   boy _____

forest _____   water _____

girl _____   I give _____

island _____   I call _____

☐ I practiced my flashcards today.

sunt

means

they are, there are

Write the Latin word that means **they are** or **there are**.

_____

- -

_____

Circle the Latin words to match the meanings.

there are	sent	sant
	sont	sunt
island	īnsula	īnsūla
	īnsala	īnsīla

☐ I practiced my flashcards today. (Add the new card.)

LET'S PRACTICE

Check the blank if the sentence is true.

    _____ 1. īnsula means **insult**.

    _____ 2. agricola means **farmer**.

    _____ 3. vocō means **crazy**.

    _____ 4. est means **we are**.

    _____ 5. puer means **boy**.

    _____ 6. aqua means **green**.

    _____ 7. sunt means **there are**.

    _____ 8. puella means **girl**.

Match the Latin words to their meanings.

___ 1. est		a. and
___ 2. dō		b. farmer
___ 3. fēmina		c. I give
___ 4. īnsula		d. boy
___ 5. agricola		e. forest
___ 6. et		f. island
___ 7. silva		g. woman
___ 8. aqua		h. there is
___ 9. puer		i. water

☐ I practiced my flashcards today.

laudō

means

I praise

Write the Latin word that means **I praise**.

_____

- -

_____

Circle the Latin words that mean **I praise**.

luadō	laudō	uladō
lāudo	laduō	leudō
aludō	laūdo	laudō
laudō	loudā	ladeō

☐ I practiced my flashcards today. (Add the new card.)

LET'S PRACTICE

Fill in the missing letters. Then write what the words mean.

īn_ul_

It means _____

_au_ō

It means _____

sil__

It means _____

———————◆·❖·◆———————

Write the meanings of the Latin words.

1. fēmina _____
2. est _____
3. dō _____
4. et _____
5. aqua _____
6. sunt _____
7. agricola _____

☐ I practiced my flashcards today.

nōn

means

not

Write the Latin word that means **not**.

_____

- -

_____

Circle the Latin words to match the meanings.

they are	not	I praise
sed	cum	laudō
sunt	amō	īnsula
silva	nōn	lingua

☐ I practiced my flashcards today. (Add the new card.)

LET'S PRACTICE

Draw lines from the words to their meanings.

fēmina	and
īnsula	island
et	woman
nōn	there are
laudō	forest
silva	I praise
sunt	not

———◆———

Unscramble the words and write them beside their meanings.

1. nuts	I give	_____
2. ōd	girl	_____
3. vails	there are	_____
4. aeullp	forest	_____

☐ I practiced my flashcards today.

ad

means

towards, to

Write the Latin word that means **towards** or **to**.

_____

– – – – – – – – – – – – – – – – – –

_____

Fill in the blanks with the Latin words from the box.

nōn	ad

– – – – – – – – – – – – – –

1. _____ means **towards**.

– – – – – – – – – – – – – –

2. _____ means **not**.

☐ I practiced my flashcards today. (Add the new card.)

LET'S PRACTICE

Circle **yes** or **no**.

yes no 1. sunt means **there are**.
yes no 2. et means **and**.
yes no 3. īnsula means **island**.
yes no 4. nōn means **not**.
yes no 5. fēmina means **woman**.
yes no 6. laudō means **I praise**.
yes no 7. ad means **news**.
yes no 8. silva means **coin**.

Circle the meanings of the Latin words.

vocō		agricola	
I sing	I call	wheat	farmer

aqua		puer	
water	green	boy	push

est		dō	
she has	she is	I do	I give

☐ I practiced my flashcards today.

52

vīta

means

life

Write the Latin word that means **life**.

_____

- - - - - - - - - - - - - - - -

_____

Connect the words to the meanings in the ovals.

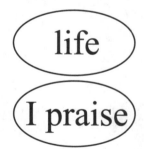

vīta   (life)   īnsula
laudō   laudō
est   (I praise)   vīta
īnsula   est

☐ I practiced my flashcards today. (Add the new card.)

LET'S PRACTICE

Write the Latin words.

and _____

woman _____

water _____

I give _____

farmer _____

it is _____

I call _____

boy _____

Draw lines from the words to their meanings.

silva	not
laudō	forest
nōn	I praise
vīta	they are
īnsula	to
sunt	life
ad	island

☐ I practiced my flashcards today.

porta

means

gate

Write the Latin word that means **gate**.

_____

- -

_____

Write the meanings of the Latin words.

1. silva _____   5. aqua _____
2. porta _____   6. et _____
3. vīta _____   7. nōn _____
4. īnsula _____   8. fēmina _____

☐ I practiced my flashcards today. (Add the new card.)

LET'S PRACTICE

Circle the Latin words to match the meanings.

and	not	island
est ad et	nauta nōn nātūra	prōvincia silva īnsula

forest	they are	life
silva patria terra	est sunt sed	laudō vīta vīlla

Fill in the missing letters. Then write what the words mean.

p_r_a

It means _____

_d

It means _____

l_u_ō

It means _____

☐ I practiced my flashcards today.

Latin Workbook - Level 2
Copyright © 1997 by Karen Mohs

memoria

means

memory

Write the Latin word that means **memory**.

_____

- -

_____

Circle **yes** or **no**.

yes   no   1. porta means **port**.
yes   no   2. ad means **from**.
yes   no   3. memoria means **memory**.
yes   no   4. vīta means **vitamin**.

☐   I practiced my flashcards today. (Add the new card.)

LET'S PRACTICE

Unscramble the words and write them beside their meanings.

1. ste

2. stun

3. trapo

4. uslīna

island _____

it is _____

there are _____

gate _____

Circle the Latin words to match the meanings.

not	non	nunt
	nōn	nōne

memory	mēmoria	memoria
	memōria	momeria

life	vita	vitā
	vītta	vīta

☐ I practiced my flashcards today.

Latin Workbook - Level 2
Copyright © 1997 by Karen Mohs

nāvigō

means

I sail

Write the Latin word that means **I sail**.

_____

– –

_____

Circle the Latin words that mean **I sail**.

nāvigo	nivāgō	navigō
nēvagō	novegō	nāvigō
nāvigō	navīgō	nōvigā
nāvōgi	nāvigō	nāvīgō

☐　I practiced my flashcards today.　(Add the new card.)

LET'S PRACTICE

Connect the words to the meanings in the ovals.

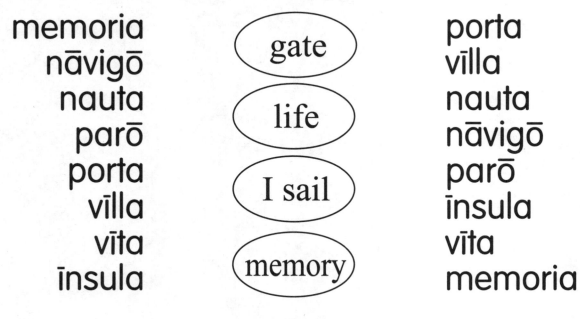

memoria
nāvigō
nauta
parō
porta
vīlla
vīta
īnsula

gate

life

I sail

memory

porta
vīlla
nauta
nāvigō
parō
īnsula
vīta
memoria

Fill in the blanks with the Latin words from the box.

nōn	laudō	ad

1. _____ means **to**.

2. _____ means **I praise**.

3. _____ means **not**.

☐ I practiced my flashcards today.

sed

means

but

Write the Latin word that means **but**.

_____

- -

_____

Match the Latin words to their meanings.

___ 1. memoria	a. but
___ 2. porta	b. I sail
___ 3. sed	c. gate
___ 4. nāvigō	d. memory

☐ I practiced my flashcards today. (Add the new card.)

LET'S PRACTICE

Circle the meanings of the Latin words.

fēmina		et	
woman	fame	eat	and

est		īnsula	
east	it is	warm	island

sunt		silva	
stamp	they are	forest	metal

———◆———

Check the blank if the sentence is true.

_____ 1. sed means **but**.

_____ 2. nōn means **none**.

_____ 3. laudō means **I praise**.

_____ 4. ad means **towards**.

_____ 5. vīta means **life**.

_____ 6. porta means **suitcase**.

_____ 7. memoria means **money**.

_____ 8. nāvigō means **I push**.

□ I practiced my flashcards today.

Latin Workbook - Level 2
Copyright © 1997 by Karen Mohs

LET'S PRACTICE

Color the hourglass green if the words mean the same.

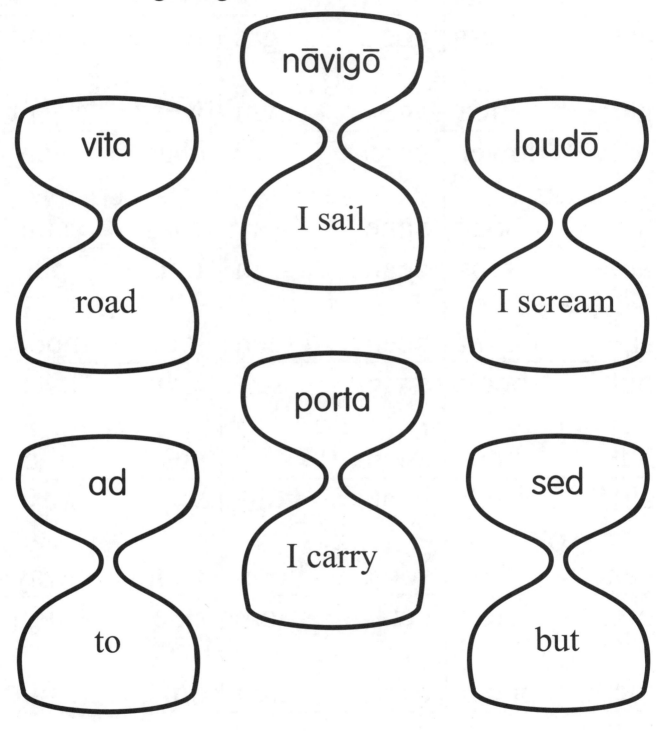

☐ I practiced my flashcards today.

LET'S PRACTICE

Circle the words that have the sounds of the Latin letters.

eat　　west **e** get　　tea	good　　gas **g** age　　gym	twine　　build **ui** weed　sweet
only　flower **au** low　　sour	greet　　see **ē** vane　　say	chair　　arc **ch** chasm　chin
hops　　tabs **bs** sips　absent	bean　　grin **ī** been　green	fun　　purr **ū** tool　　mood
put　　book **u** hut　　boot	swing　　suit **su** swim　　sure	firm　　oven **f** vast　　after
able　　back **b** pan　　lips	boat　　hope **ō** some　　hook	van　　wash **v** valley　away
broil　　toy **oe** toe　　poem	cent　　acre **c** care　　arch	ride　　sign **i** dip　　spin

☐　I practiced my flashcards today.

Latin Workbook - Level 2
Copyright © 1997 by Karen Mohs

fortūna

means

fortune, chance

Write the Latin word that means **fortune** or **chance**.

_____

- -

_____

Circle the Latin words that mean **fortune** or **chance**.

fartūna	fūrtōna	fortūna
fortuna	fōrtūna	furtāna
fōrtūna	fotrūna	fōrtūnā
fortūna	fortūna	fornūta

☐ I practiced my flashcards today. (Add the new card.)

LET'S PRACTICE

Fill in the blanks with the Latin words from the box.

nōn	vīta	ad

_____

1. _____ means **life**.

_____

2. _____ means **not**.

_____

3. _____ means **towards**.

Circle the Latin words to match the meanings.

life	I sail	chance
vīta	nātūra	fīlius
vīlla	nāvigō	fēmina
via	nauta	fortūna

but	memory	gate
silva	littera	porta
sunt	memoria	portō
sed	lingua	parō

☐ I practiced my flashcards today.

via

means

road, way

Write the Latin word that means **road** or **way**.

_____

- -

_____

Draw lines from the words to their meanings.

via	fortune
sed	I sail
fortūna	way
nāvigō	but

☐ I practiced my flashcards today. (Add the new card.)

LET'S PRACTICE

Write the meanings of the Latin words.

1. memoria _____

2. porta _____

3. vīta _____

4. sed _____

5. nāvigō _____

6. via _____

7. fortūna _____

———————◆————◆————

Unscramble the words and write them beside their meanings.

1. ōnn   towards _____

2. aēinmf   not _____

3. da   I praise _____

4. aōudl   woman _____

☐ I practiced my flashcards today.

Latin Workbook - Level 2
Copyright © 1997 by Karen Mohs

portō

means

I carry

Write the Latin word that means **I carry**.

_____

- -

_____

Circle the meanings of the Latin words.

nāvigō		portō	
sailor	I sail	I carry	gate

fortūna		via	
treasure	chance	life	road

☐ I practiced my flashcards today. (Add the new card.)

LET'S PRACTICE

Circle **yes** or **no**.

yes no 1. memoria means **album**.
yes no 2. nāvigō means **I sail**.
yes no 3. porta means **I carry**.
yes no 4. fortūna means **bank**.
yes no 5. vīta means **life**.
yes no 6. via means **way**.
yes no 7. portō means **gate**.
yes no 8. sed means **but**.

Write the Latin words.

forest _____

towards _____

island _____

and _____

not _____

I praise _____

water _____

they are _____

☐ I practiced my flashcards today.

quid

means

what
(a question)

Write the Latin word that means **what** (a question).

_____

- -

_____

Circle the Latin words to match the meanings.

what?	quid	quide
	qued	guid
I carry	partō	purtō
	portā	portō

☐ I practiced my flashcards today. (Add the new card.)

LET'S PRACTICE

Match the Latin words to their meanings.

___	1. nāvigō	a.	towards
___	2. memoria	b.	gate
___	3. sunt	c.	there are
___	4. laudō	d.	life
___	5. porta	e.	I sail
___	6. ad	f.	memory
___	7. vīta	g.	I praise
___	8. sed	h.	not
___	9. nōn	i.	but

Connect the words to the meanings in the ovals.

fēmina	chance	fortūna
quid		via
ubi	what?	porta
fortūna		vīta
portō	I carry	quid
vīta		ubi
porta	way	fēmina
via		portō

☐ I practiced my flashcards today.

tuba

means

trumpet

Write the Latin word that means **trumpet**.

_____

– –

_____

Fill in the missing letters. Then write what the words mean.

_u_a

It means _____

_ui_

It means _____

☐ I practiced my flashcards today. (Add the new card.)

LET'S PRACTICE

Check the blank if the sentence is true.

_____ 1. tuba means **trumpet**.
_____ 2. nāvigō means **I sail**.
_____ 3. fortūna means **chance**.
_____ 4. sed means **I spoke**.
_____ 5. portō means **I open**.
_____ 6. quid means **what?**
_____ 7. via means **air**.
_____ 8. porta means **gate**.

———————•◆◆◆•———————

Fill in the blanks with the Latin words from the box.

puella	memoria	vīta

1. _____ means **girl**.

2. _____ means **memory**.

3. _____ means **life**.

☐ I practiced my flashcards today.

ager

means

field, territory

Write the Latin word that means **field** or **territory**.

_____

- -

_____

Write the meanings of the Latin words.

1. sed _____
2. via _____
3. nāvigō _____
4. fortūna _____

5. quid _____
6. ager _____
7. tuba _____
8. portō _____

☐ I practiced my flashcards today. (Add the new card.)

LET'S PRACTICE

Circle the Latin words to match the meanings.

towards	gate	not
et	porta	nauta
ad	poēta	sed
dō	patria	nōn

memory	I praise	life
nātūra	īnsula	vīta
prōvincia	littera	ubi
memoria	laudō	quid

Circle **yes** or **no**.

yes no 1. sed means **word**.

yes no 2. nāvigō means **I sail**.

yes no 3. tuba means **trumpet**.

yes no 4. via means **pill**.

yes no 5. portō means **I eat**.

yes no 6. quid means **slime**.

yes no 7. ager means **territory**.

yes no 8. fortūna means **chest**.

☐ I practiced my flashcards today.

Latin Workbook - Level 2
Copyright © 1997 by Karen Mohs

parō

means

I prepare, I prepare for

Write the Latin word that means **I prepare** or **I prepare for**.

_____

- -

_____

Unscramble the words and write them beside their meanings.

- - - - - - - - - - - - - - - -

1. rōpa   territory _____

_____

- - - - - - - - - - - - - - - -

2. rage   I prepare _____

☐ I practiced my flashcards today. (Add the new card.)

LET'S PRACTICE

Circle the meanings of the Latin words.

porta		nāvigō	
gate	dock	I sail	I guide

ad		memoria	
to	math	album	memory

vīta		sed	
grow	life	but	seed

Draw lines from the words to their meanings.

parō	I carry
portō	what?
quid	I prepare
via	chance
ager	trumpet
tuba	way
fortūna	territory

☐ I practiced my flashcards today.

Latin Workbook - Level 2
Copyright © 1997 by Karen Mohs

amīcus

means

friend

Write the Latin word that means **friend**.

_____

- -

_____

Fill in the blanks with the Latin words from the box.

parō	amīcus

1. _____ means **I prepare**.

2. _____ means **friend**.

☐ I practiced my flashcards today. (Add the new card.)

LET'S PRACTICE

Write the Latin words.

I prepare _____   chance _____

but _____   friend _____

trumpet _____   I carry _____

I sail _____   memory _____

Circle the Latin words to match the meanings.

road way	vīa	via
	vea	vēa

field territory	agger	aeger
	ager	āger

what?	quid	qiud
	qeud	qued

☐ I practiced my flashcards today.

Latin Workbook - Level 2
Copyright © 1997 by Karen Mohs

spectō

means

I look at

Write the Latin word that means **I look at**.

_____

- -

_____

Circle **yes** or **no**.

yes no 1. ager means **field**.

yes no 2. spectō means **I look at**.

yes no 3. parō means **I eat**.

yes no 4. amīcus means **minus**.

☐ I practiced my flashcards today. (Add the new card.)

LET'S PRACTICE

Connect the words to the meanings in the ovals.

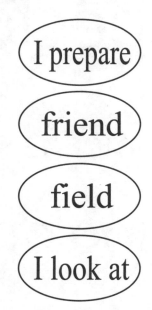

parō   I prepare   spectō
amīcitia   ager
aqua   friend   portō
ager   amīcitia
portō   field   amīcus
amīcus   silva
silva   I look at   parō
spectō   aqua

Check the blank if the sentence is true.

_____ 1. parō means **I cut**.

_____ 2. fortūna means **chance**.

_____ 3. ager means **mad**.

_____ 4. via means **road**.

_____ 5. spectō means **I wash**.

_____ 6. portō means **I carry**.

_____ 7. tuba means **straw**.

_____ 8. quid means **fish**.

_____ 9. sed means **but**.

☐ I practiced my flashcards today.

nātūra

means

nature

Write the Latin word that means **nature**.

_____

- -

_____

Match the Latin words to their meanings.

___ 1. parō	a.	nature
___ 2. spectō	b.	friend
___ 3. amīcus	c.	I prepare for
___ 4. nātūra	d.	I look at

☐ I practiced my flashcards today. (Add the new card.)

Copyright © 1997 by Karen Mohs

83

LET'S PRACTICE

Fill in the missing letters. Then write what the words mean.

n_t_ra

It means _____

a__r

It means _____

_m__us

It means _____

———————◆◆◆———————

Circle the meanings of the Latin words.

portō		spectō	
I carry	I drink	I study	I look at

tuba		via	
pipe	trumpet	life	road

parō		quid	
I peel	I prepare	what?	who?

☐ I practiced my flashcards today.

LET'S PRACTICE

Connect the bubbles to the bubble pipes.

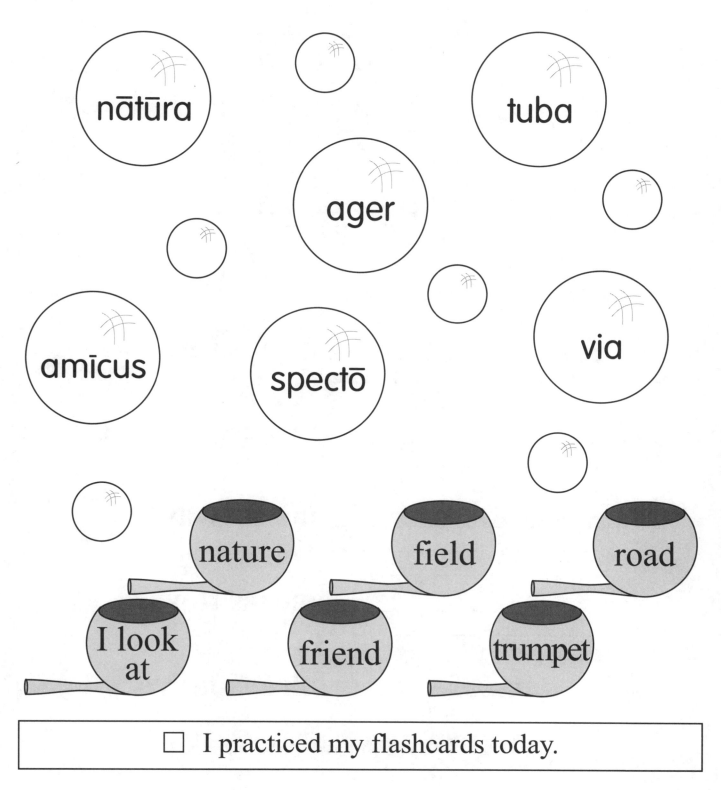

☐ I practiced my flashcards today.

PUZZLE TIME

Circle five Latin words. Write them below.

f	v	l	a	u	d	ō
g	i	t	d	p	ō	p
p	a	r	ō	k	c	i
s	m	p	ē	n	h	d

1. _____ means **I praise**.

2. _____ means **I prepare**.

3. _____ means **way**.

4. _____ means **toward**.

5. _____ means **I give**.

☐ I practiced my flashcards today.

campus

means

field, plain

Write the Latin word that means **field** or **plain**.

_____

_ _

_____

Circle the Latin words to match the meanings.

I look at	nature	field
silva	porta	gladius
pugnō	nātūra	cum
spectō	nauta	campus

☐ I practiced my flashcards today. (Add the new card.)

LET'S PRACTICE

Fill in the blanks with the Latin words from the box.

via	portō	quid

_____

1. _____ means **road**.

2. _____ means **what?**

3. _____ means **I carry**.

Write the meanings of the Latin words.

1. nātūra _____
2. campus _____
3. spectō _____
4. amīcus _____
5. tuba _____
6. ager _____
7. parō _____

☐ I practiced my flashcards today.

occupō

means

I seize, I capture

Write the Latin word that means **I seize** or **I capture**.

Circle the Latin words that mean **I seize** or **I capture**.

occupō	āccupō	occupō
ocupō	occupō	ōccupō
occūpō	ocuppō	occūpo
ocoupō	occapō	accupō

☐ I practiced my flashcards today. (Add the new card.)

LET'S PRACTICE

Unscramble the words and write them beside their meanings.

1. aiv   life _____

2. iuqd   I carry _____

3. rōtop   road _____

4. taīv   what? _____

Circle **yes** or **no**.

yes   no   1. spectō means **I look at**.
yes   no   2. parō means **I prepare for**.
yes   no   3. amīcus means **friend**.
yes   no   4. ager means **field**.
yes   no   5. occupō means **I sleep**.
yes   no   6. nātūra means **nation**.
yes   no   7. tuba means **bathtub**.
yes   no   8. campus means **tent**.

☐ I practiced my flashcards today.

cum

means

with

Write the Latin word that means **with**.

_____

- -

_____

Write the Latin words.

I seize _____   nature _____

plain _____   with _____

☐ I practiced my flashcards today. (Add the new card.)

LET'S PRACTICE

Draw lines from the words to their meanings.

ager	plain
quid	territory
cum	what?
nātūra	with
tuba	nature
amīcus	trumpet
campus	friend

———◆◆◆———

Fill in the missing letters. Then write what the words mean.

s_e_tō

It means _____

o_cu_ō

It means _____

p_r_

It means _____

☐ I practiced my flashcards today.

Latin Workbook - Level 2
Copyright © 1997 by Karen Mohs

nauta

means

sailor

Write the Latin word that means **sailor**.

_____

- -

_____

Connect the words to the meanings in the ovals.

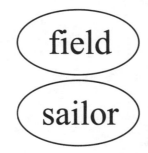

nauta   campus
amīcus   nātūra
nātūra   amīcus
campus   nauta

☐ I practiced my flashcards today. (Add the new card.)

LET'S PRACTICE

Circle the Latin words to match the meanings.

friend	ammīcus	amīccus
	amīcus	amīecus

sailor	neuta	nauta
	natua	nueta

I look at	speccō	spertō
	spettō	spectō

Match the Latin words to their meanings.

___ 1. quid   a. I capture
___ 2. nātūra   b. plain
___ 3. portō   c. I prepare for
___ 4. parō   d. territory
___ 5. occupō   e. trumpet
___ 6. tuba   f. what?
___ 7. ager   g. nature
___ 8. cum   h. I carry
___ 9. campus   i. with

☐ I practiced my flashcards today.

vīlla

means

farmhouse

Write the Latin word that means **farmhouse**.

_____

— —

_____

Check the blank if the sentence is true.

_____ 1. nātūra means **nature**.

_____ 2. spectō means **I expect**.

_____ 3. cum means **with**.

_____ 4. vīlla means **village**.

☐ I practiced my flashcards today. (Add the new card.)

LET'S PRACTICE

Write the meanings of the Latin words.

1. nātūra   _____

2. ager   _____

3. parō   _____

4. spectō   _____

5. nauta   _____

6. amīcus   _____

7. occupō   _____

Fill in the missing letters. Then write what the words mean.

īll

It means _____

ca__pu_

It means _____

c____

It means _____

☐ I practiced my flashcards today.

littera

means

letter

Write the Latin word that means **letter**.

_____

- - - - - - - - - - - - - - - - - -

_____

Circle the Latin words that mean **letter**.

literra	lettira	letera
līttera	lattira	littera
littera	littera	litterā
littēra	lēttera	lāttera

☐ I practiced my flashcards today. (Add the new card.)

LET'S PRACTICE

Circle **yes** or **no**.

yes	no	1.	nauta means **sailor**.
yes	no	2.	littera means **letter**.
yes	no	3.	vīlla means **wish**.
yes	no	4.	occupō means **work**.
yes	no	5.	nātūra means **nature**.
yes	no	6.	campus means **plain**.
yes	no	7.	spectō means **careful**.
yes	no	8.	cum means **arrive**.

Match the Latin words to their meanings.

___ 1. fortūna	a.	I prepare
___ 2. amīcus	b.	chance
___ 3. ad	c.	life
___ 4. via	d.	trumpet
___ 5. parō	e.	gate
___ 6. vīta	f.	way
___ 7. sed	g.	towards
___ 8. tuba	h.	friend
___ 9. porta	i.	but

☐ I practiced my flashcards today.

ubi

means

where
(a question)

Write the Latin word that means **where** (a question).

_____

_ _

_____

Draw lines from the words to their meanings.

nauta	sailor
littera	farmhouse
vīlla	where?
ubi	letter

☐ I practiced my flashcards today. (Add the new card.)

LET'S PRACTICE

Circle the Latin words to match the meanings.

farmhouse	with	where?
prōvincia	nōn	ager
via	cum	ubi
vīlla	quid	tuba

I capture	sailor	letter
occupō	nauta	spectō
portō	puer	littera
laudō	nāvigō	lingua

Write the Latin words.

what? _____   friend _____

I look at _____   plain _____

territory _____   trumpet _____

I prepare _____   nature _____

☐ I practiced my flashcards today.

fīlius

means

son

Write the Latin word that means **son**.

_____

- -

_____

Circle the meanings of the Latin words.

vīlla		littera	
farmhouse	village	litter	letter

fīlius		nauta	
file	son	sailor	bad

☐ I practiced my flashcards today. (Add the new card.)

LET'S PRACTICE

Unscramble the words and write them beside their meanings.

1. scaīmu   nature _____

2. cetsōp   I look at _____

3. ratānū   trumpet _____

4. atbu   friend _____

Circle the Latin words to match the meanings.

I seize I capture	occūpo	ocupō
	ocuppō	occupō

sailor	nauta	naūta
	nautā	nuata

son	filēus	filīus
	fīlius	filuis

☐ I practiced my flashcards today.

patria

means

country, native land

Write the Latin word that means **country** or **native land**.

_____

- -

_____

Connect the words to the meanings in the ovals.

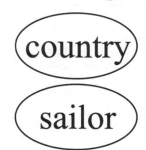

patria   country   nauta
via   filius
filius   sailor   via
nauta   patria

☐   I practiced my flashcards today. (Add the new card.)

LET'S PRACTICE

Check the blank if the sentence is true.

_____ 1. occupō means **I sit**.
_____ 2. ubi means **why?**
_____ 3. nauta means **sailor**.
_____ 4. fīlius means **son**.
_____ 5. littera means **letter**.
_____ 6. cum means **with**.
_____ 7. vīlla means **farmhouse**.
_____ 8. campus means **camp**.

———◆———

Fill in the blanks with the Latin words from the box.

nātūra	spectō	patria

1. _____ means **country**.

2. _____ means **nature**.

3. _____ means **I look at**.

☐ I practiced my flashcards today.

fīlia

means

daughter

Write the Latin word that means **daughter**.

_____

- -

_____

Circle the Latin words to match the meanings.

daughter	where?	country
fīlia	ubi	prōvincia
fēmina	via	porta
fīlius	quid	patria

☐ I practiced my flashcards today. (Add the new card.)

LET'S PRACTICE

Fill in the missing letters. Then write what the words mean.

īli

It means _____

_itt_r_

It means _____

_īli_s

It means _____

———————— •◆•◆•◆• ————————

Write the meanings of the Latin words.

1. cum _____
2. occupō _____
3. ubi _____
4. campus _____
5. vīlla _____
6. patria _____
7. nauta _____

☐ I practiced my flashcards today.

LET'S PRACTICE

Draw a picture of an amīcus in an ager looking ad a vīlla.

☐ I practiced my flashcards today.

PUZZLE TIME

Circle five Latin words. Write them below.

v	ī	l	l	a	z	a
i	ȳ	ā	s	g	ū	q
a	m	h	ī	e	x	u
c	p	a	t	r	i	a

1. _____ means **farmhouse**.

2. _____ means **native land**.

3. _____ means **road**.

4. _____ means **territory**.

5. _____ means **water**.

☐ I practiced my flashcards today.

Latin Workbook - Level 2
Copyright © 1997 by Karen Mohs

amīcitia

means

friendship

Write the Latin word that means **friendship**.

_____

- -

_____

Circle the Latin words that mean **friendship**.

amīcitia	amīcītia	amītícia
amicitia	amícītia	amícītīa
acīmitia	amícitia	amícitia
āmīcitia	āmícitīa	amīcitai

☐ I practiced my flashcards today. (Add the new card.)

LET'S PRACTICE

Draw lines from the words to their meanings.

amīcitia	I look at
spectō	friendship
occupō	field
campus	I seize
parō	nature
cum	I prepare for
nātūra	with

Circle **yes** or **no**.

yes no 1. nauta means **nature**.
yes no 2. vīlla means **farmhouse**.
yes no 3. amīcus means **friend**.
yes no 4. fīlia means **pony**.
yes no 5. patria means **I clap**.
yes no 6. ubi means **where?**
yes no 7. littera means **clutter**.
yes no 8. fīlius means **son**.

☐ I practiced my flashcards today.

amō

means

I love, I like

Write the Latin word that means **I love** or **I like**.

_____

- -

_____

Write the Latin words.

where? _____   son _____

I love _____   letter _____

☐ I practiced my flashcards today. (Add the new card.)

LET'S PRACTICE

Circle the Latin words to match the meanings.

with	cum	cōm
	cūm	com

friendship	amīcittia	amīccitia
	amīcitia	ammīcitia

farmhouse	vīlia	vīllia
	vīla	vīlla

Unscramble the words and write them beside their meanings.

1. pōocuc   I love _____

2. ōam   where? _____

3. aīlvl   I seize _____

4. ibu   farmhouse _____

☐ I practiced my flashcards today.

112

lingua

means

tongue, language

Write the Latin word that means **tongue** or **language**.

_____

– –

_____

Fill in the blanks with the Latin words from the box.

amō	lingua

1. _____ means **language**.

2. _____ means **I like**.

☐ I practiced my flashcards today. (Add the new card.)

LET'S PRACTICE

Circle the meanings of the Latin words.

amīcitia		puer	
show	friendship	boy	son

lingua		amō	
line	tongue	I like	bullet

vīlla		vocō	
farmhouse	valley	word	I call

Match the Latin words to their meanings.

___ 1. patria	a. field
___ 2. fīlia	b. sailor
___ 3. occupō	c. son
___ 4. littera	d. where?
___ 5. cum	e. native land
___ 6. ubi	f. I seize
___ 7. nauta	g. letter
___ 8. campus	h. daughter
___ 9. fīlius	i. with

☐ I practiced my flashcards today.

Latin Workbook - Level 2
Copyright © 1997 by Karen Mohs

equus

means

horse

Write the Latin word that means **horse**.

_____

- -

_____

Check the blank if the sentence is true.

_____ 1. amīcitia means **happiness**.

_____ 2. equus means **horse**.

_____ 3. lingua means **language**.

_____ 4. amō means **I am**.

☐ I practiced my flashcards today. (Add the new card.)

LET'S PRACTICE

Connect the words to the meanings in the ovals.

lingua		amō
amīcus	friendship	annus
amīcitia		equus
annus	horse	est
equus		littera
littera	I love	lingua
est		amīcus
amō	tongue	amīcitia

Circle the meanings of the Latin words.

patria		littera	
father	country	letter	trash

ubi		fīlius	
where?	which?	boy	son

fīlia		vīlla	
daughter	girl	farmhouse	village

☐ I practiced my flashcards today.

poēta

means

poet

Write the Latin word that means **poet**.

_____

- -

_____

Fill in the missing letters. Then write what the words mean.

e_ū_s

It means _____

po_t_

It means _____

☐ I practiced my flashcards today. (Add the new card.)

LET'S PRACTICE

Unscramble the words and write them beside their meanings.

1. ingōāv   sailor _____

2. tunaa   I sail _____

3. rimomea   farmer _____

4. liacgroa   memory _____

Draw lines from the words to their meanings.

equus	native land
amīcitia	horse
lingua	language
patria	friendship
poēta	I like
amō	daughter
fīlia	poet

☐ I practiced my flashcards today.

Latin Workbook - Level 2
Copyright © 1997 by Karen Mohs

annus

means

year

Write the Latin word that means **year**.

_____

- -

_____

Write the meanings of the Latin words.

1. fīlius _____
2. poēta _____
3. vīlla _____
4. fīlia _____
5. ubi _____
6. littera _____
7. equus _____
8. annus _____

☐ I practiced my flashcards today. (Add the new card.)

LET'S PRACTICE

Write the Latin words.

son _____ I like _____

country _____ daughter _____

where? _____ letter _____

farmhouse _____ friend _____

Connect the words to the meanings in the ovals.

poēta	(year)	amō
patria		annus
equus	(poet)	est
laudō		laudō
annus	(horse)	equus
lingua		lingua
est	(tongue)	poēta
amō		patria

☐ I practiced my flashcards today.

pugnō

means

I fight

Write the Latin word that means **I fight**.

_____

– –

_____

Circle **yes** or **no**.

yes   no   1. annus means **year**.
yes   no   2. poēta means **I write**.
yes   no   3. pugnō means **I pick**.
yes   no   4. equus means **horse**.

☐   I practiced my flashcards today. (Add the new card.)

LET'S PRACTICE

Fill in the blanks with the Latin words from the box.

patria	amīcitia	fīlia

1. _____ means **friendship**.

2. _____ means **daughter**.

3. _____ means **native land**.

Circle the Latin words to match the meanings.

I love	I fight	language
amō	puella	littera
amīcitia	pugnō	laudō
amīcus	puer	lingua

year	poet	horse
aqua	parō	est
ager	poēta	equus
annus	porta	et

☐ I practiced my flashcards today.

terra

means

earth, land

Write the Latin word that means **earth** or **land**.

_____

- -

_____

Circle the Latin words to match the meanings.

I fight	pognē	pagnā
	pugnō	pagnō
earth	teara	tera
	terra	tirra

☐ I practiced my flashcards today. (Add the new card.)

LET'S PRACTICE

Match the Latin words to their meanings.

___	1. littera	a. farmhouse
___	2. annus	b. where?
___	3. patria	c. year
___	4. vīlla	d. I capture
___	5. occupō	e. country
___	6. fīlius	f. letter
___	7. nauta	g. with
___	8. ubi	h. son
___	9. cum	i. sailor

Check the blank if the sentence is true.

_____ 1. poēta means **poet**.

_____ 2. pugnō means **I fight**.

_____ 3. amō means **I fire**.

_____ 4. amīcitia means **friendship**.

_____ 5. equus means **horse**.

_____ 6. fīlia means **son**.

_____ 7. lingua means **noodle**.

_____ 8. terra means **land**.

☐ I practiced my flashcards today.

gladius

means

sword

Write the Latin word that means **sword**.

_____

- -

_____

Circle the Latin words that mean **sword**.

glādius	glādīus	gildaus
galdius	gladuis	gladius
gladīus	gladius	glādiūs
gladius	gladiūs	glidaus

☐ I practiced my flashcards today. (Add the new card.)

LET'S PRACTICE

Circle the Latin words to match the meanings.

I fight	poet	earth
laudō	puella	patria
spectō	poēta	terra
pugnō	porta	agricola

sword	year	horse
gladius	annus	campus
puer	filius	equus
fortūna	ad	amīcus

———◆———

Fill in the blanks with the Latin words from the box.

amīcitia	amō	lingua

1. _____ means **I love**.

2. _____ means **tongue**.

3. _____ means **friendship**.

☐ I practiced my flashcards today.

126

Latin Workbook - Level 2
Copyright © 1997 by Karen Mohs

prōvincia

means

province

Write the Latin word that means **province**.

_____

– –

_____

Draw lines from the words to their meanings.

gladius	land
pugnō	I fight
prōvincia	province
terra	sword

☐ I practiced my flashcards today. (Add the new card.)

LET'S PRACTICE

Write the meanings of the Latin words.

1. poēta   _____
2. annus   _____
3. prōvincia   _____
4. terra   _____
5. pugnō   _____
6. gladius   _____
7. equus   _____

Unscramble the words and write them beside their meanings.

1. aaiprt | plain   _____
                        _____
2. mcu | language _____
                        _____
3. aucsmp | country   _____
                        _____
4. aiugnl | with   _____

☐ I practiced my flashcards today.

LET'S PRACTICE

Write the Latin words.

plain _____   country _____

friend _____   with _____

girl _____   son _____

daughter _____   I like _____

Circle **yes** or **no**.

yes   no   1. pugnō means **I stop**.
yes   no   2. lingua means **debate**.
yes   no   3. prōvincia means **province**.
yes   no   4. annus means **year**.
yes   no   5. equus means **horse**.
yes   no   6. poēta means **poet**.
yes   no   7. gladius means **gift**.
yes   no   8. terra means **plant**.

☐ I practiced my flashcards today.

LET'S PRACTICE

Match the Latin words to their meanings.

___	1. filia	a.	I fight
___	2. amīcus	b.	boy
___	3. lingua	c.	poet
___	4. terra	d.	earth
___	5. pugnō	e.	friend
___	6. poēta	f.	sword
___	7. amō	g.	tongue
___	8. puer	h.	I like
___	9. gladius	i.	daughter

Circle the Latin words to match the meanings.

year	annūs	unnas
	annus	anins

province	provincia	provinnia
	provēncia	prōvincia

horse	ēquus	equus
	eqqus	equis

☐ I practiced my flashcards today.

LET'S PRACTICE

Connect the words to the meanings in the ovals.

tuba   poet   pugnō
poēta   dō
puella   I fight   gladius
dō   tuba
gladius   sword   poēta
pugnō   īnsula
īnsula   horse   equus
equus   puella

Fill in the missing letters. Then write what the words mean.

pr__in_ia

It means _____

a_nu_

It means _____

t_r_a

It means _____

☐ I practiced my flashcards today.

LET'S PRACTICE

Check the blank if the sentence is true.

_____ 1. pugnō means **I fight**.
_____ 2. annus means **year**.
_____ 3. lingua means **tongue**.
_____ 4. equus means **add**.
_____ 5. terra means **afraid**.
_____ 6. prōvincia means **shout**.
_____ 7. gladius means **happy**.
_____ 8. amō means **I like**.

Circle the meanings of the Latin words.

fīlia		ubi	
daughter	colt	why?	where?

fīlius		amīcus	
son	file	friend	less

poēta		patria	
manner	poet	country	flower

☐ I practiced my flashcards today.

LET'S PRACTICE

Write the Latin words on the chimneys.

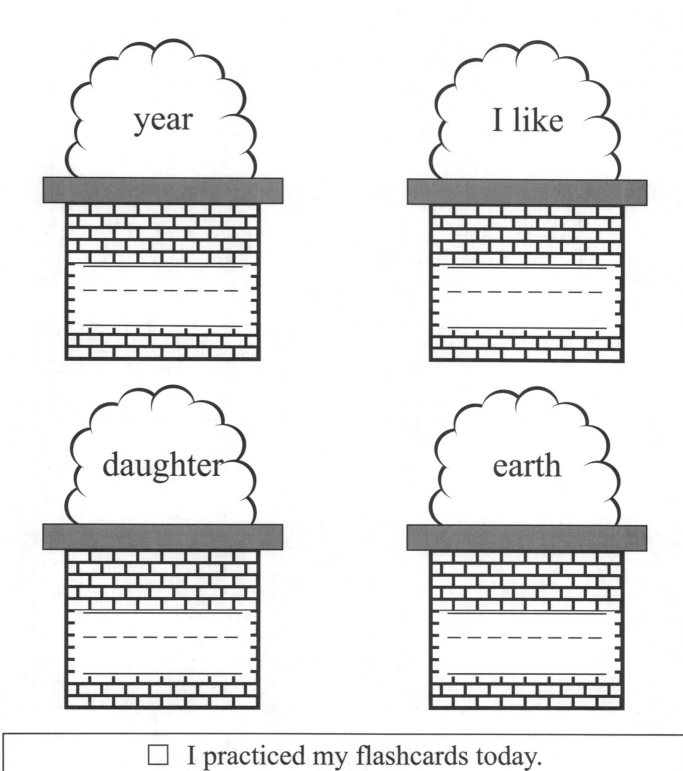

year

I like

daughter

earth

☐ I practiced my flashcards today.

PUZZLE TIME

Think of the meanings of the English words. Then write the Latin words on the puzzle below.

across	down
1. friendship	1. I love
2. province	3. I call
7. I give	4. sailor
9. I sail	5. not
11. plain	6. I carry
12. I prepare for	8. life
	10. way

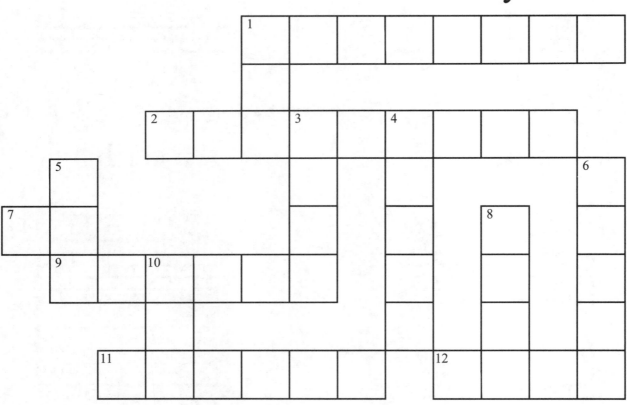

☐ I practiced my flashcards today.

Latin Workbook - Level 2
Copyright © 1997 by Karen Mohs

FINAL ALPHABET REVIEW

Write the Latin letters for the sounds.

1. Latin _____ sounds like **l** in *land*.

2. Latin _____ sounds like **dz** in *adze*.

3. Latin _____ sounds like **a** in *father*.

4. Latin _____ sounds like **i** in *sit*.

5. Latin _____ sounds like **qu** in *quit*.

6. Latin _____ sounds like **r** in *run*.

7. Latin _____ sounds like **ey** in *obey*.

8. Latin _____ sounds like **i** in *machine*.

9. Latin _____ sounds like **e** in *bet*.

10. Latin _____ sounds like **f** in *fan*.

☐ I practiced my flashcards today.

FINAL ALPHABET REVIEW

Write the Latin letters for the sounds.

1. Latin _____ sounds like **o** in *omit*.

2. Latin _____ sounds like **k** in *king*.

3. Latin _____ is a shorter sound than Ȳ ȳ.

4. Latin _____ sounds like **b** in *boy*.

5. Latin _____ sounds like **u** in *rule*.

6. Latin _____ sounds like **p** in *pit*.

7. Latin _____ is a longer sound than Y y.

8. Latin _____ sounds like **u** in *put*.

9. Latin _____ sounds like **g** in *go*.

10. Latin _____ sounds like **d** in *dog*.

□ I practiced my flashcards today.

FINAL ALPHABET REVIEW

Write the Latin letters for the sounds.

1. Latin _____ sounds like **a** in *idea*.

2. Latin _____ sounds like **s** in *sit*.

3. Latin _____ sounds like **t** in *tag*.

4. Latin _____ sounds like **n** in *nut*.

5. Latin _____ sounds like **m** in *man*.

6. Latin _____ sounds like **o** in *note*.

7. Latin _____ sounds like **c** in *cat*.

8. Latin _____ sounds like **ks** in *socks*.

9. Latin _____ sounds like **w** in *way*.

10. Latin _____ sounds like **h** in *hat*.

☐ I practiced my flashcards today.

FINAL DIPHTHONG REVIEW

Write the Latin letters for the sounds.

1. Latin _____ sounds like **ay-oo** (in one syllable).

2. Latin _____ sounds like **ow** in **now**.

3. Latin _____ sounds like **uee** in **queen**.

4. Latin _____ sounds like **aye**.

5. Latin _____ sounds like **oy** in **joy**.

6. Latin _____ sounds like **ei** in **neighbor**.

☐ I practiced my flashcards today.

138

FINAL SPECIAL CONSONANTS REVIEW

Write the Latin letters for the sounds.

1. Latin _____ sounds like **gu** in *anguish*.

2. Latin _____ sounds like **su** in *suave*.

3. Latin _____ sounds like *ps*.

4. Latin _____ sounds like **y** in *youth*.

5. Latin _____ sounds like **ch** in *character*.

6. Latin _____ sounds like **ph** in *phone*.

7. Latin _____ sounds like **th** in *thick*.

8. Latin _____ sounds like *pt*.

☐ I practiced my flashcards today.

FINAL VOCABULARY REVIEW

Write the Latin words.

_____

1. I prepare for   _____

2. forest   _____

3. memory   _____

4. year   _____

5. I fight   _____

6. son   _____

7. language   _____

8. territory   _____

9. sailor   _____

10. and   _____

☐ I practiced my flashcards today.

Latin Workbook - Level 2
Copyright © 1997 by Karen Mohs

FINAL VOCABULARY REVIEW

Write the Latin words.

1. poet

2. there are

3. I like

4. where?

5. plain

6. girl

7. I capture

8. island

9. I call

10. I give

☐ I practiced my flashcards today.

FINAL VOCABULARY REVIEW

Write the Latin words.

1. letter

2. I look at

3. I carry

4. with

5. farmhouse

6. there is

7. sword

8. friendship

9. not

10. trumpet

☐ I practiced my flashcards today.

FINAL VOCABULARY REVIEW

Write the Latin words.

1. I sail

2. fortune

3. but

4. I praise

5. farmer

6. gate

7. land

8. woman

9. road

10. horse

☐ I practiced my flashcards today.

FINAL VOCABULARY REVIEW

Write the Latin words.

1. native land

2. what?

3. life

4. friend

5. towards

6. province

7. boy

8. water

9. nature

10. daughter

☐ I practiced my flashcards today.

Latin - English Glossary

a
ad - towards or to (51)
ager - field or territory (75)
agricola - farmer (29)
amīcitia - friendship (109)
amīcus - friend (79)
amō - I love or I like (111)
annus - year (119)
aqua - water (31)

c
campus - field or plain (87)
cum - with (91)

d
dō - I give (27)

e
equus - horse (115)
est - he is, she is, it is, there is (33)
et - and (37)

f
fēmina - woman (35)
filia - daughter (105)
filius - son (101)
fortūna - fortune or chance (65)

g
gladius - sword (125)

i
īnsula - island (43)

l
laudō - I praise (47)
lingua - tongue or language (113)
littera - letter (97)

m
memoria - memory (57)

n
nātūra - nature (83)
nauta - sailor (93)
nāvigō - I sail (59)
nōn - not (49)

o
occupō - I seize or I capture (89)

p
parō - I prepare or I prepare for (77)
patria - country or native land (103)
poēta - poet (117)
porta - gate (55)
portō - I carry (69)
prōvincia - province (127)
puella - girl (21)
puer - boy (25)
pugnō - I fight (121)

q
quid - what? (71)

s
sed - but (61)
silva - forest (39)
spectō - I look at (81)
sunt - they are, there are (45)

t
terra - earth or land (123)
tuba - trumpet (73)

u
ubi - where? (99)

v
via - road or way (67)
vīlla - farmhouse (95)
vīta - life (53)
vocō - I call (23)

Note: The number in parentheses indicates the page on which the vocabulary word is introduced.

APPENDIX

English - Latin Glossary

a
and - et
are - sunt

b
boy - puer
but - sed

c
call - vocō
capture - occupō
carry - portō
chance - fortūna
country - patria

d
daughter - filia

e
earth - terra

f
farmer - agricola
farmhouse - vīlla
field - ager, campus
fight - pugnō
forest - silva
fortune - fortūna
friend - amīcus
friendship - amīcitia

g
gate - porta
girl - puella
give - dō

h
horse - equus

i
is - est
island - īnsula

l
land - terra
language - lingua
letter - littera
life - vīta
like - amō
look at - spectō
love - amō

m
memory - memoria

n
native land - patria
nature - nātūra
not - nōn

p
plain - campus
poet - poēta
praise - laudō
prepare - parō
prepare for - parō
province - prōvincia

r
road - via

s
sail - nāvigō
sailor - nauta
seize - occupō
son - filius
sword - gladius

t
territory - ager
to - ad
tongue - lingua
towards - ad
trumpet - tuba

w
water - aqua
way - via
what? - quid
where? - ubi
with - cum
woman - fēmina

y
year - annus

APPENDIX

Latin Alphabet

Capital Letter	Small Letter	Pronunciation		Capital Letter	Small Letter	Pronunciation
Ā	ā	**a** in *father*		N	n	**n** in *nut*
A	a	**a** in *idea*		Ō**	ō**	**o** in *note*
B	b	**b** in *boy*		O**	o**	**o** in *omit*
C	c	**c** in *cat*		P	p	**p** in *pit*
D	d	**d** in *dog*		Q	q	**qu** in *quit*
Ē	ē	**ey** in *obey*		R	r	**r** in *run*
E	e	**e** in *bet*		S	s	**s** in *sit*
F	f	**f** in *fan*		T	t	**t** in *tag*
G	g	**g** in *go*		Ū	ū	**u** in *rule*
H	h	**h** in *hat*		U	u	**u** in *put*
Ī	ī	**i** in *machine*		V	v	**w** in *way*
I*	i*	**i** in *sit*		X	x	**ks** in *socks*
K	k	**k** in *king*		Ȳ	ȳ	form lips to say "**oo**" but say "**ee**" instead (held longer)
L	l	**l** in *land*		Y	y	form lips to say "**oo**" but say "**ee**" instead (held shorter)
M	m	**m** in *man*		Z	z	**dz** in *adze*

*When functioning as a consonant, i has the sound of **y** in *youth*. (See **Special Consonants** below.)

**The ō and the o both have a long o sound, but the ō is held longer.

Special Sounds

Diphthongs

Letters	Pronunciation
ae	*aye*
au	**ow** in *now*
ei	**ei** in *neighbor*
eu	*ay-oo*
oe	**oy** in *joy*
ui	**uee** in *queen*

Special Consonants

Letters	Pronunciation
bs	*ps*
bt	*pt*
ch	**ch** in *character*
gu	**gu** in *anguish*
i	**y** in *youth*
ph	**ph** in *phone*
su	**su** in *suave*
th	**th** in *thick*

APPENDIX

Flashcard Tips

1. Remember to practice flashcards daily.

2. Do not move ahead in the workbook if your student is struggling for mastery. Review the flashcards every day until your student is confident and ready to learn more.

"Latin's Not So Tough!"
Level Two
Feedback Form

Dear Friend of Greek 'n' Stuff:

Please use the following form to give us your feedback regarding this workbook. Mail your comments to:

> Greek 'n' Stuff
> P.O. Box 882
> Moline, IL 61266-0882

If you prefer, you may send your comments via fax (309-796-2706).

What did you enjoy about this book?

_____
_____
_____
_____

In what ways could this book be more effective?

_____
_____
_____
_____

Circle "yes" beside the Learning Aids which you found helpful in your studies. We would also like to know what you especially liked about each (and/or any suggestions you may have for improvement).

yes   "Answers Only" key _____

yes   "Full Text" key _____

yes   Quizzes/Exams _____

yes   "Flashcards on a Ring" _____

yes   Pronunciation CD/tape _____

yes   Greek 'n' Stuff's Internet homepage (**www.greeknstuff.com**) with its "Greek and Latin Words of the Month" _____

(front)	(back)
Ā ā	(Start on page 1.) (Level 2) **a** in *father*
A a	(Page 1) (Level 2) **a** in *idea*
B b	(Page 1) (Level 2) **b** in *boy*
C c	(Page 2) (Level 2) **c** in *cat*
D d	(Page 2) (Level 2) **d** in *dog*
Ē ē	(Page 2) (Level 2) **ey** in *obey*

(front)	(back)
E e	(Page 3) **e** in *bet* (Level 2)
F f	(Page 3) **f** in *fan* (Level 2)
G g	(Page 3) **g** in *go* (Level 2)
H h	(Page 4) **h** in *hat* (Level 2)
Ī ī	(Page 4) **i** in *machine* (Level 2)
Ĭ ĭ	(Page 4) **i** in *sit* (Level 2)

(front)	(back)
K k	(Page 5) (Level 2) **k** in ***king***
L l	(Page 5) (Level 2) **l** in ***land***
M m	(Page 5) (Level 2) **m** in ***man***
N n	(Page 6) (Level 2) **n** in ***nut***
Ō ō	(Page 6) (Level 2) **o** in ***note***
O o	(Page 6) (Level 2) **o** in ***omit***

(front)	(back)
P p	(Page 7) (Level 2) **p** in *pit*
Qu qu	(Page 7) (Level 2) **qu** in *quit*
R r	(Page 7) (Level 2) **r** in *run*
S s	(Page 8) (Level 2) **s** in *sit*
T t	(Page 8) (Level 2) **t** in *tag*
Ū ū	(Page 8) (Level 2) **u** in *rule*

(front)	(back)
U u	(Page 9) (Level 2) **u** in *put*
V v	(Page 9) (Level 2) **w** in *way*
X x	(Page 9) (Level 2) **ks** in *socks*
Ȳ ȳ	(Page 10) (Level 2) Form your lips to say **oo**, but say **ee** instead. (held longer than y)
Y y	(Page 10) (Level 2) Form your lips to say **oo**, but say **ee** instead. (held shorter than ȳ)
Z z	(Page 10) (Level 2) **dz** in *adze*

(front)	(back)
ɑe	(Page 12)　　　　　(Level 2)　　　　***"aye"***
ɑu	(Page 12)　　　　　(Level 2)　　**ow** in ***now***
ei	(Page 12)　　　　　(Level 2)　　**ei** in ***neighbor***
eu	(Page 13)　　　　　(Level 2)　***"ay-oo"*** (in one syllable)
oe	(Page 13)　　　　　(Level 2)　　**oy** in ***joy***
ui	(Page 13)　　　　　(Level 2)　　**uee** in ***queen***

(front)	(back)
bs	(Page 15) (Level 2) *"ps"*
bt	(Page 15) (Level 2) *"pt"*
ch	(Page 15) (Level 2) **ch** in *character*
gu	(Page 16) (Level 2) **gu** in *anguish*
i	(Page 16) (Level 2) **y** in *youth*
ph	(Page 16) (Level 2) **ph** in *phone*

(front)	(back)
su	(Page 17) (Level 2) **su** in ***suave***
th	(Page 17) (Level 2) **th** in ***thick***
puella	(Page 21) (Level 2) girl
vocō	(Page 23) (Level 2) I call
puer	(Page 25) (Level 2) boy
dō	(Page 27) (Level 2) I give

(front)	(back)
agricola	(Page 29) (Level 2) farmer
aqua	(Page 31) (Level 2) water
est	(Page 33) (Level 2) he is, she is, it is, there is
fēmina	(Page 35) (Level 2) woman
et	(Page 37) (Level 2) and
silva	(Page 39) (Level 2) forest

(front)	(back)
īnsula	(Page 43) (Level 2) island
sunt	(Page 45) (Level 2) they are, there are
laudō	(Page 47) (Level 2) I praise
nōn	(Page 49) (Level 2) not
ad	(Page 51) (Level 2) towards, to
vīta	(Page 53) (Level 2) life

(front)	(back)
porta	(Page 55) (Level 2) gate
memoria	(Page 57) (Level 2) memory
nāvigō	(Page 59) (Level 2) I sail
sed	(Page 61) (Level 2) but
fortūna	(Page 65) (Level 2) fortune, chance
via	(Page 67) (Level 2) road, way

(front)	(back)
portō	(Page 69) (Level 2) I carry
quid	(Page 71) (Level 2) what (a question)
tuba	(Page 73) (Level 2) trumpet
ager	(Page 75) (Level 2) field, territory
parō	(Page 77) (Level 2) I prepare, I prepare for
amīcus	(Page 79) (Level 2) friend

(front)	(back)
spectō	(Page 81) (Level 2) I look at
nātūra	(Page 83) (Level 2) nature
campus	(Page 87) (Level 2) field, plain
occupō	(Page 89) (Level 2) I seize, I capture
cum	(Page 91) (Level 2) with
nauta	(Page 93) (Level 2) sailor

(front)	(back)
vīlla	(Page 95) (Level 2) farmhouse
littera	(Page 97) (Level 2) letter
ubi	(Page 99) (Level 2) where (a question)
fīlius	(Page 101) (Level 2) son
patria	(Page 103) (Level 2) country, native land
fīlia	(Page 105) (Level 2) daughter

(front)	(back)
amīcitia	(Page 109) (Level 2) friendship
amō	(Page 111) (Level 2) I love, I like
lingua	(Page 113) (Level 2) tongue, language
equus	(Page 115) (Level 2) horse
poēta	(Page 117) (Level 2) poet
annus	(Page 119) (Level 2) year

(front)	(back)
pugnō	(Page 121) (Level 2) I fight
terra	(Page 123) (Level 2) earth, land
gladius	(Page 125) (Level 2) sword
prōvincia	(Page 127) (Level 2) province